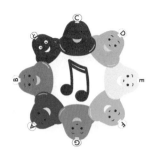

Preschool Prodigies
CHAPTER THREE
3

By: Robert and Samantha Young
Illustrations: Robert Young with art licensed at FreePik.com

Published by: Young Music, LLC
ISBN: 978-0999210116
Copyright © 2017
Preschool Prodigies and Young Music, LLC
2358 Dutch Neck Road
Smyrna, DE 19977

Prodigies Playground

THIS BOOK BELONGS TO:

_____

Dear families & teachers,

Welcome back to Preschool Prodigies. Prepare for more musical fun in Chapter Three!

In this chapter, your learner will learn their second chord, G Major. We'll play both the C Major and G Major chords, compare them with listening games, chord building activities and Roman numeral practice.

Chords are a more difficult concept, and playing more than one musical note at a time can be challenging; however, research and methods surrounding early pitch development show us that early practice with the 3 Major chords (I, IV and V) are essential to developing a strong sense of pitch.

To make approaching chords a little easier for kids, here are a couple tips:

1. If a chord lesson has 5 different notes, split the five bells up among multiple players. Then, children only have to worry about 1 or 2 notes. This will reinforce cooperative play with their peers, turn taking and ensemble playing, while simplifying the physical challenge of playing multiple bells.

2. Don't be afraid to simplify the chord. If a chord is written as 3 notes and you can only play 2, that's okay! Experiment with what pairs you like best.

3. Focus on learning the notes of the chord, but don't get hung up on the order. With the C Major Bells, we only have one octave of notes, so the order of the chord may seem inconsistent or slightly random. Don't fret! The general mood of the chord will still shine through.

4. Use the speed control options inside the Playground videos to slow down any lessons your learner is having trouble with.

As always, encourage your learner to practice consistently and often. Create lots of opportunities to work music into your day and always approach the subject postively.

Happy Musicing!

– Mr. Rob & Prodigies Team

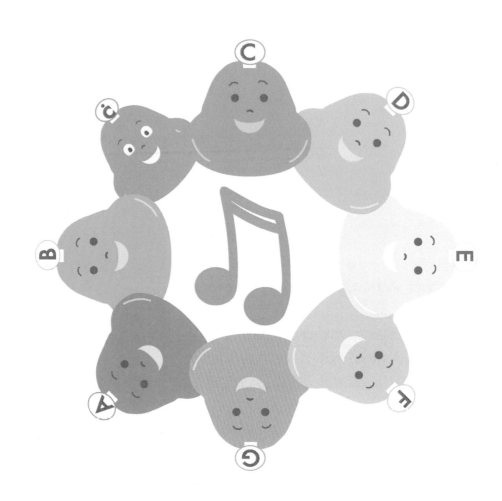

Chapter 3 ♫ Section 1: C & G, Best Friends ♫ Lesson Guide

Objective
By the end of this section, students should be able to differentiate between C and G and be able to play both whole and half notes.

Overview
In this section, students explore the notes C and G while incorporating whole notes into their play.

Essential Question
How can a student differentiate between the notes C and G?

Instruction Tips
Some teachers prefer to cut the notes out for the first activity before students arrive. This is a great way to save time if necessary; however, if the students cut out the notes themselves, they can develop their fine motor skills.

Materials
- C Bell • G Bell
- Red Crayon • Teal Crayon
- C & G, BFFs Video Access
- Workbook pages: 6-13
- Scissors
- Tape or Glue

Table of Contents

Complementary Activities
Play a call and response game using the melody your learner created in the first activity.

Section 3.1 Video Annotations

0:00 This is a fun song to highlight the relationship between Low C and G. Make sure you remove the other bells so that your learner has only the Red Low C and the Teal G. This limits the chance of errors and strengthens the important tonal relationship between Do and Sol, or the 1 and 5 notes.

0:17 Pause and let your learner know that Mr. Rob will be playing different rhythms in this song. It's okay if they don't get the rhythm right away, but they should listen carerfully and try to play along when they can.

2:56 Pause and let your learner practice playing the notes loudly and softly.

C & G, BFFs
Lesson 3.1

Practice singing and playing with Do and Sol in this simple song!

1st Verse   G   and   C   un   –

2nd Verse   Which   one   do   you

Repeat Song and
Sing 2nd Verse

1st Verse   til   the   end.

2nd Verse   like   the   best?

Whole Notes and Half Notes

Cut out the whole notes and half notes on the next page, and arrange them over the blank measures to write your own song.

half note
(2 beats)

G

Whole Notes and Half Notes

Cut out the whole notes and half notes on this page,
and arrange them over the blank measures to write your
own song.

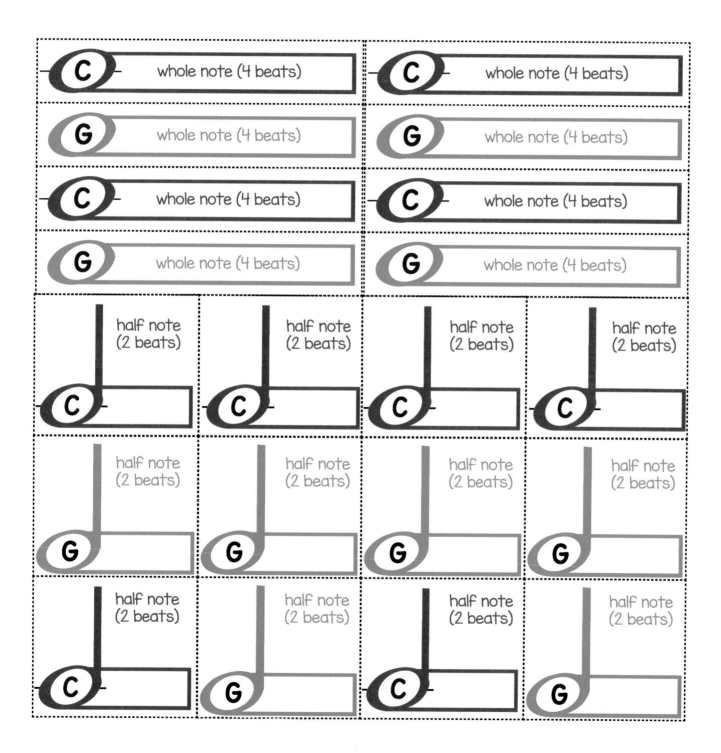

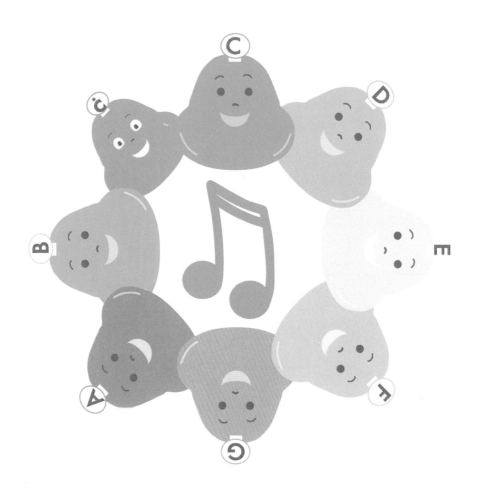

C & G Coloring

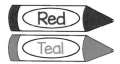

Play the pattern of short and long notes below with your C & G bells. Then sing it with the Do & Sol hand-signs. After that, color in C boxes red & G boxes teal.

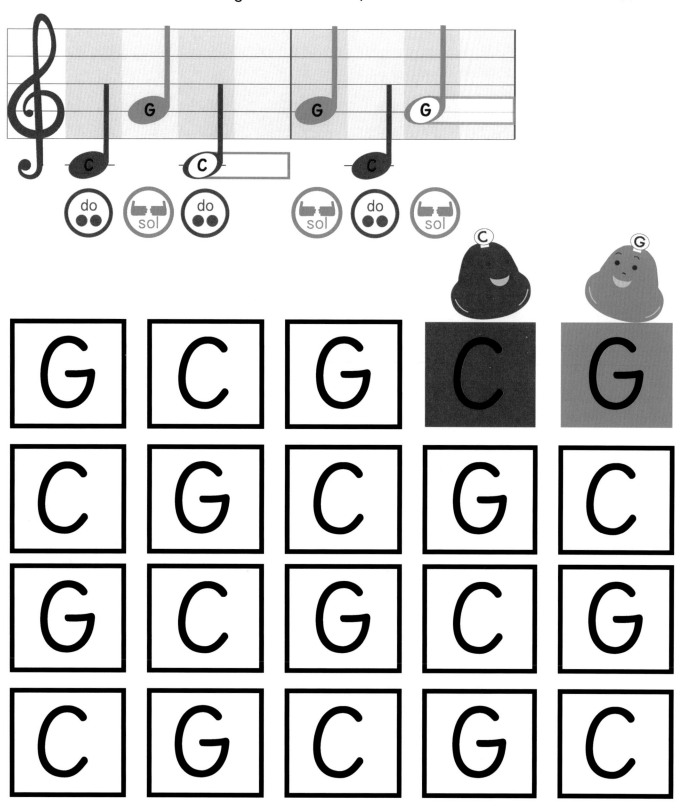

Patterns

Let's practice with some C and G patterns.
First, complete the pattern by writing C or G in the blank space.
Then play the pattern on your bells!

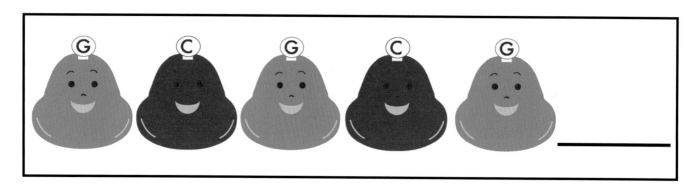

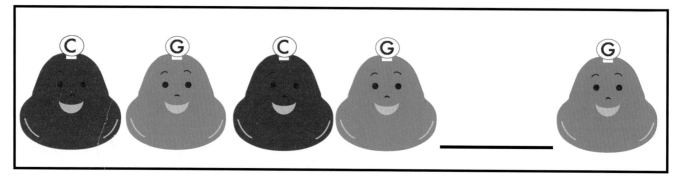

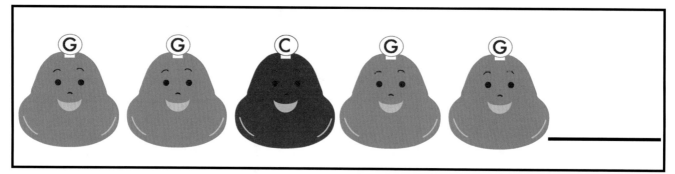

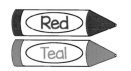

Circle the Gs & Cs

1. Practice writing the words below.
2. Put a **red circle** around the words that start with C.
3. Put a teal circle around the words that start with G.

chick   window   gift

giraffe   coat   street

flower   grass   corn

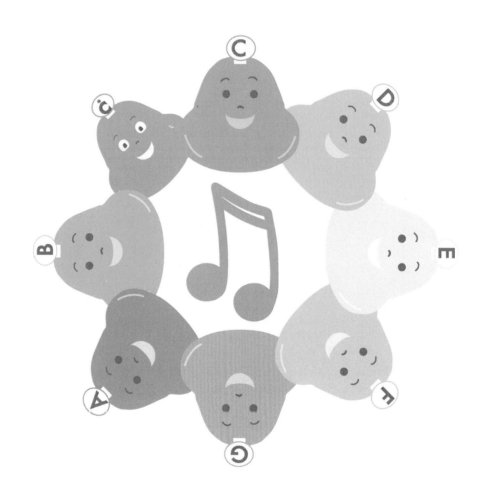

Chapter 3 ♫ Section 2: The Wheels on the Bus ♫ Lesson Guide

Objective

By the end of this section, students should be able to clap a quarter note pattern in time.

Overview

In this section, students play a simplified version of "The Wheels on the Bus", using C, G and quarter notes.

Essential Question

How can a student use C and G to simplify "The Wheels on the Bus"?

Instruction Tips

If the students have trouble playing along with the quarter note exercise, try clapping and singing along with a metronome. Just search "metronome" on Google if you don't have one.

Materials

- C Bell • G Bell
- Red Crayon • Teal Crayon
- The Wheels on the Bus Video Access
- Workbook pages: 16-21
- Scissors
- Tape or Glue

Table of Contents

Complementary Activities

Ask your learner to play their 1, 5, 8 Song or their quarter note song. Challenge them to add lyrics to their songs.

Section 3.2 Video Annotations

0:00 In this simplified version of The Wheels on the Bus, students only play C and G to represent the I chord and the V chord. Make sure that your learner only has those two bells out.

1:07 Pause here and explain to your learner(s) that they should be playing the notes when they get to the centers of the Do and Sol sections.

2:19 Pause and ask your learner what the name of the "shh" note is in music.

The Wheels on the Bus

(two note pattern)

Lesson 3.2

Below is a simple arrangement for the Wheels on the Bus. It may seem easy and different from the full song, but we will get to playing the full song soon! To make sure your ready for the harder version, spend some time practicing this arrangement with a metronome! Try to play along with the beep of the metronome at 80-90 BPM.

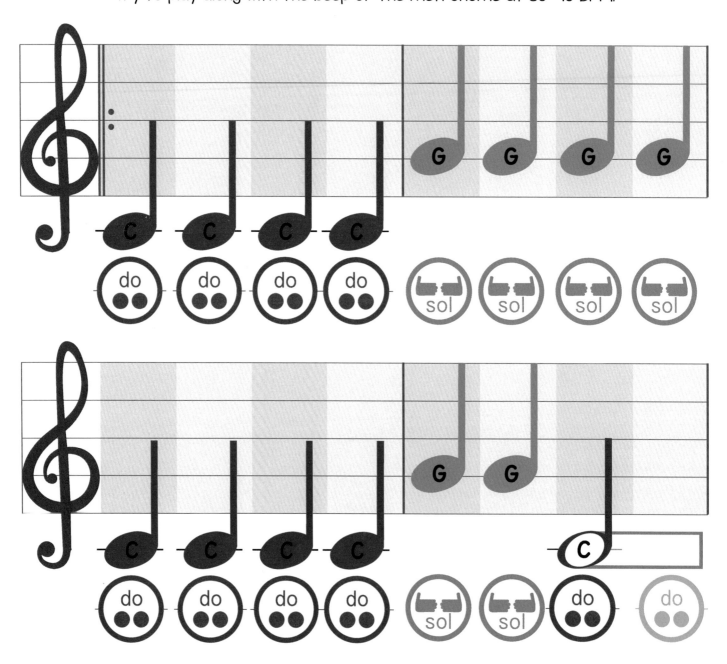

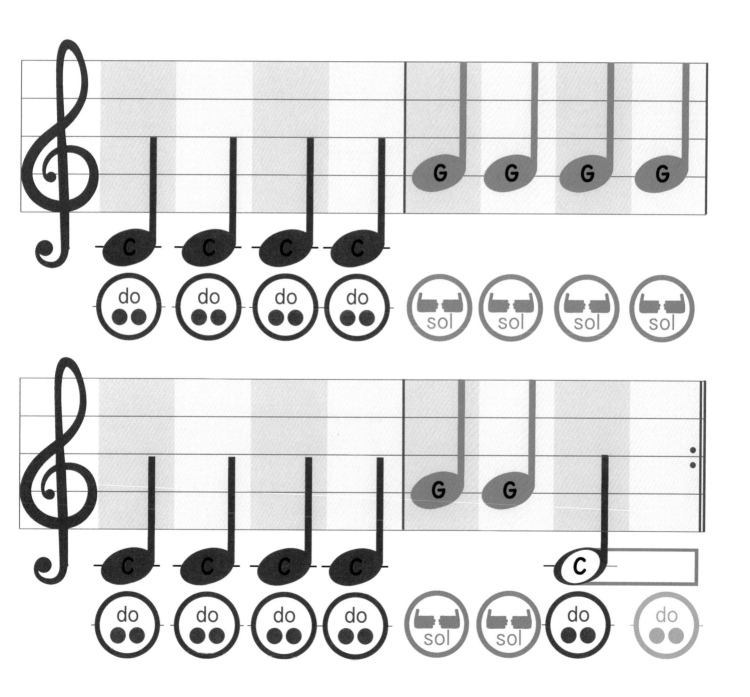

Do and Sol Hand-Signs

Adding hand-signs to our musical notes makes learning, feeling and singing the notes more physical and more fun!

You can hang this hand-sign poster in your music room!
Use it to practice with Do and Sol. Try singing and hand-signing back and forth slowly. Then practice a little bit faster and see just how fast you can go!

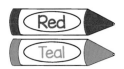

Count the Wheels

Can you count the tires in each pile? Write the number below each stack, and then play the bells and sing the numbers!

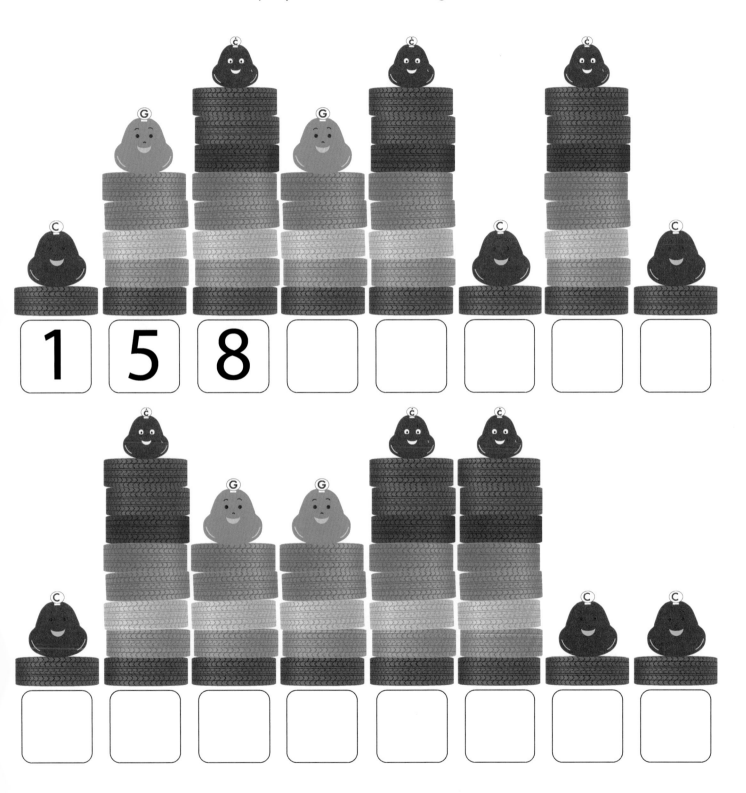

| 1 | 5 | 8 | | | | | |

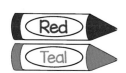

Compose a 1, 5, 8 Song

Practice writing the numbers 1, 5 and 8!

Only put one number in each box! Then try to play your song with your bells.
Challenge: Write the words to a song underneath the numbers and try to sing
it. You can use the different letters of your name instead of words!

1 5 5 8 8

8   5

5

8   1

Quarter Notes

Have you ever tried to clap and count at the same time? Try it below!

Repeat the top line again! It's a great way to practice keeping a steady beat!

Let's try it again with the Red Bell!

Now let's try it with the **quarter note.**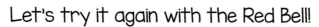

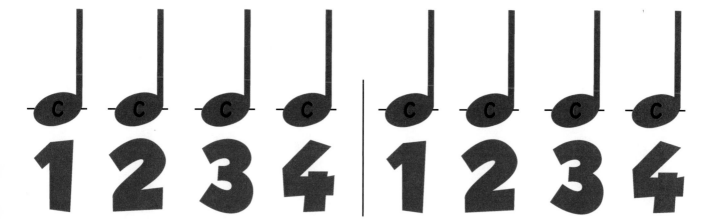

Quarter Notes

Cut out the quarter notes on the next page and paste them on top
of the gray boxes to make a quarter note song!

Quarter Notes

Cut out the quarter notes below and paste them on top
of the gray boxes on the previous page to make a quarter note song!

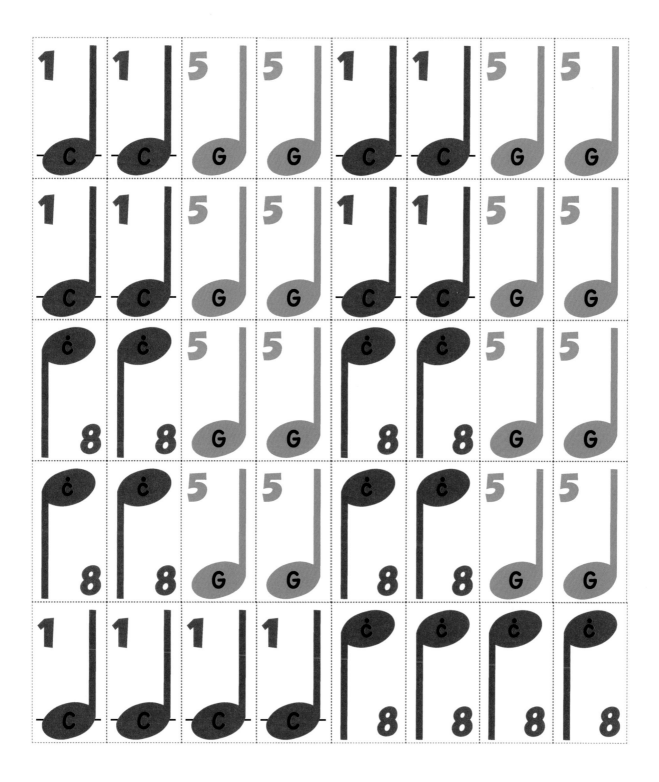

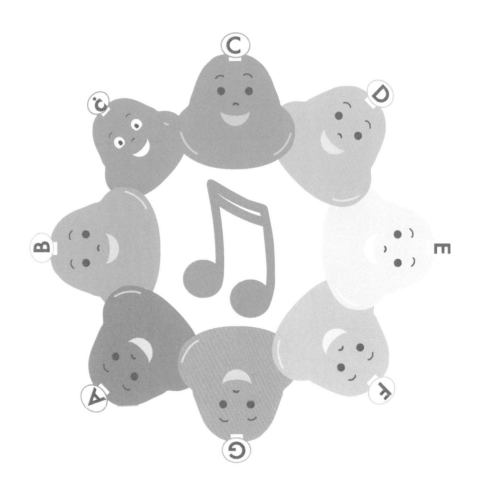

Chapter 3 🎵 Section 3: Chords: C & G 🎵 Lesson Guide

Objective

By the end of this section, students should be able to both identify the notes in the C Major Chord and the G Major Chord, and write the Roman numeral for 1 and 5.

Overview

In this section, students practice with the C and G Major Chord, and learn Roman numerals to reference the chords.

Essential Question

How can a student play and reference a C and G Major Chord?

Instruction Tips

Some children may need to reposition the bells in order to play chords. Let them experiment with different positions and see what's most comfortable.

Materials

- B Bell • C Bell • D Bell
- E Bell • G Bell
- Red Crayon
- Teal Crayon
- Chords: C & G Video Access
- Workbook pages: 27-33

Table of Contents

Complementary Activities

Play a call and response song using the C Major Chord and G Major Chord.

Section 3.3 Video Annotations

0:50 Pause here and make sure each child has his or her bells set up correctly. Ask your learner why we call the C chord the I chord and the G chord the V chord.

1:01 Pause here and explain to the students that they should be playing each note right as the stem on the small pumpkin rolls behind the large pumpkin.

1:37 Mr. Rob begins to sing with the numbers.

2:24 Mr. Rob begins to play with chords.

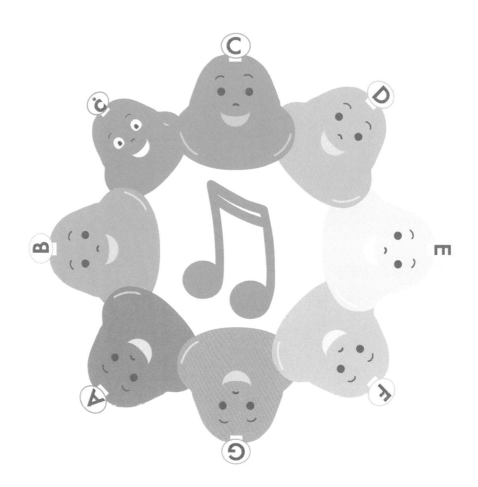

Chord Mat
I – V
C Major & G Major

Chords: C and G
Lesson 3.3

Try singing the broken chords in this song using the letter names!

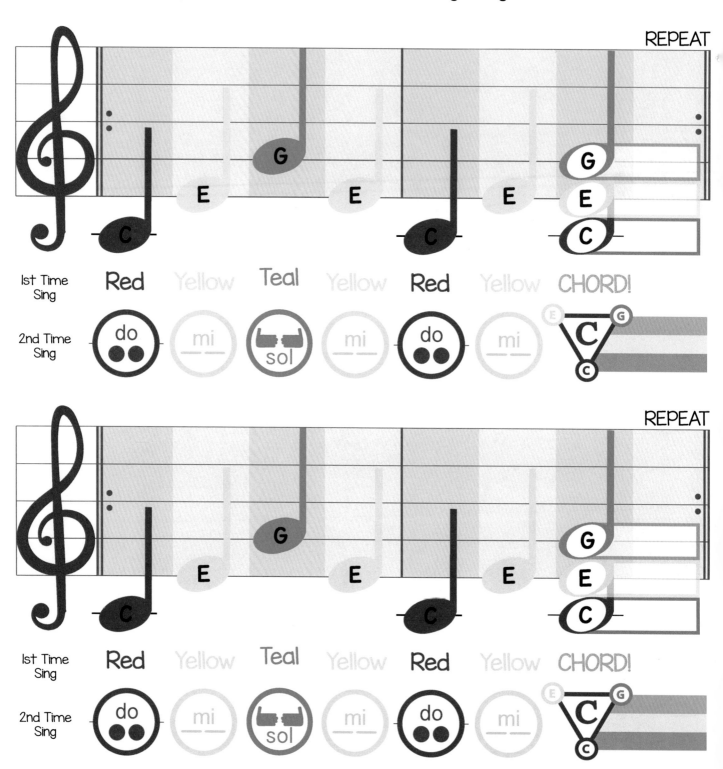

REPEAT

REPEAT

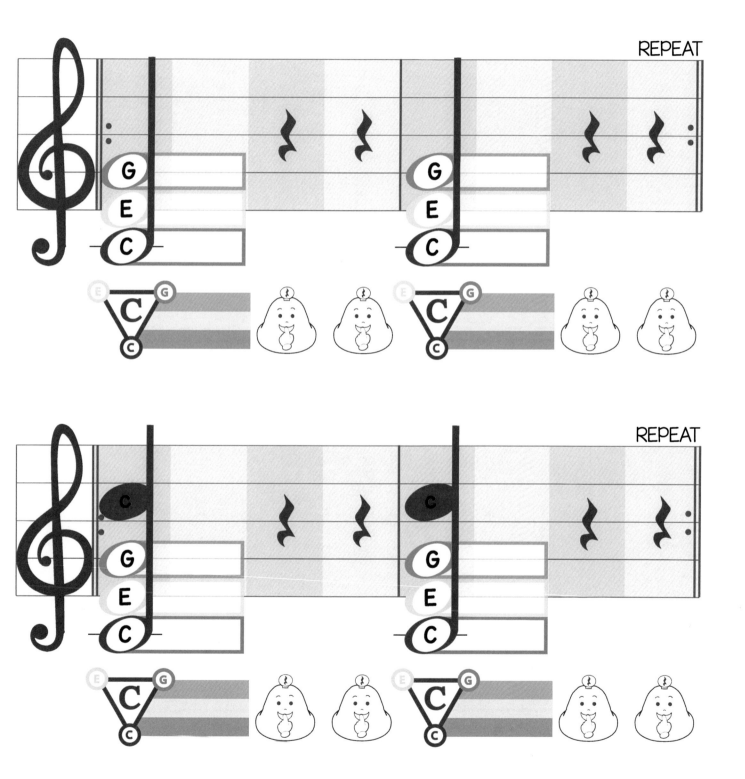

Preschool Prodigies – Chapter Three Workbook **29**

Meet the Roman Numerals

The "C Major Chord" is also called the "One Chord." To make the "One Chord," we use the Roman numeral for I, which looks like an I.

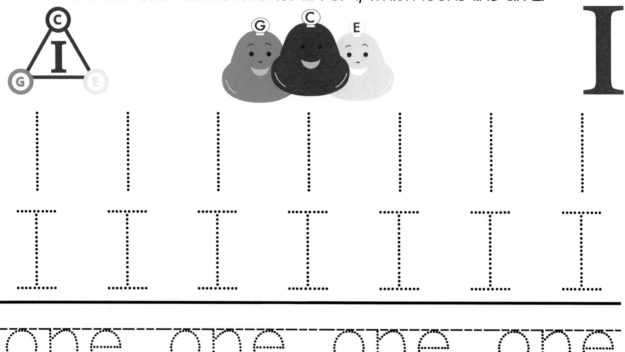

| | | | | | | | | | | |

I I I I I I

one one one one

The "G Major Chord" starts on bell 5, so we call it the "Five Chord," and we use the Roman numeral for 5, which looks like a V.

5 5 5 5 5 5 5 5

V V V V V V V V

five five five five

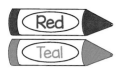

Counting Bells

Count the bells in each circle and then trace the Roman numeral I or V.

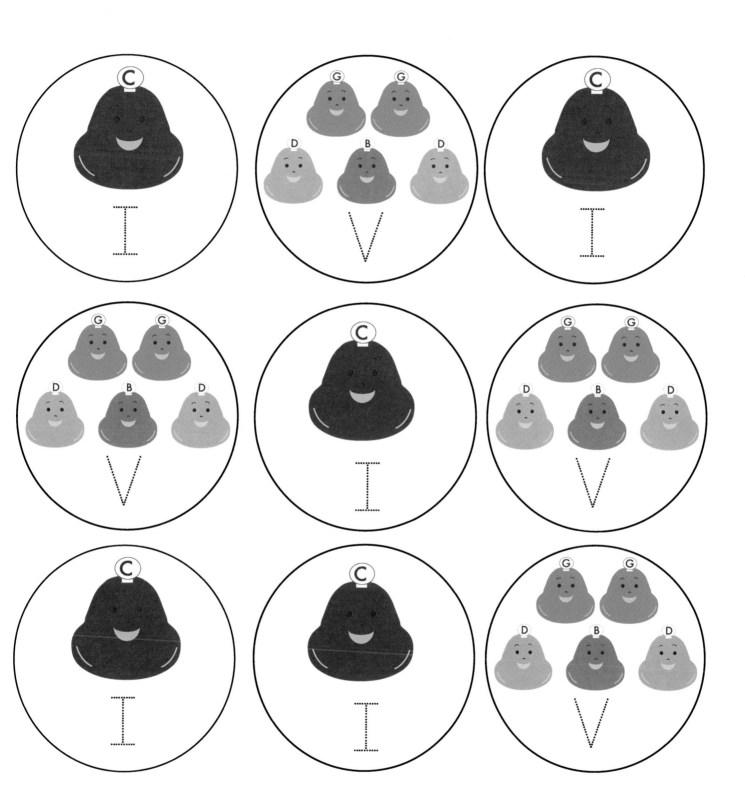

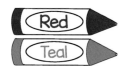

Roman Numerals

Let's practice writing our Roman Numerals, I (one) and V (five).
Start by tracing the number on the left. Then trace the Roman
numeral. Finally, try writing the Roman numeral (I or V) on the blank lines.

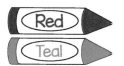

I & V

Write the number represented by each Roman numeral and group of pictures.
If there is one starfish, write I.
If there are five starfish, write V.

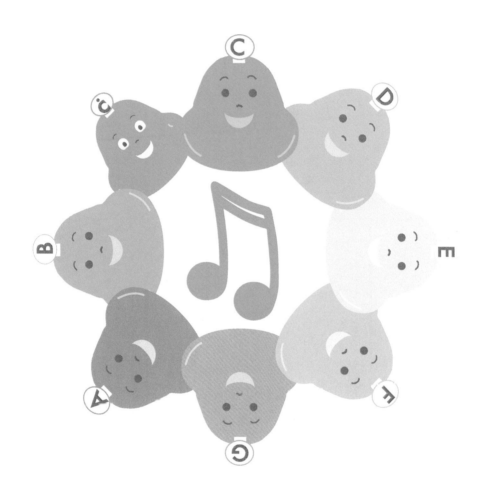

Chapter 3 ♫ Section R: Beet & Cherry ♫ Lesson Guide

Objective

By the end of this section, students should be able to clap, tap or stomp both a quarter note and an eighth note.

Overview

In this section, students will continue to practice eighth & quarter notes. Students will count with beets & cherrys, tas & titis and numbers.

Essential Question

How can a student count quarter and eighth notes?

Instruction Tips

This version of Beet and Cherry is slightly faster. Take advantage of the playback speed feature on the video if the pace is too fast for students. For an extra challenge, try speeding it up.

Materials

- Beet & Cherry Video Access
- Workbook pages: 36-43

Table of Contents

Complementary Activities

Try singing other words instead of Beet and Cherry to the tune of "Beet and Cherry", like the words in the Rhythm sort.

Section 3.R Video Annotations

0:21 Pause here and explain to students how they should participate (clapping, tapping, boomwhacking, etc.).

1:27 Mr. Rob sings with Tas and Ti-Tis here instead of Beets and Cherries.

2:03 Mr. Rob sings with numbers instead of Tas and Ti-Tis.

Beet & Cherry
Lesson 3.R

☆☆☆☆☆

Sing the chorus to Sweet Beets while tapping a steady beat. Then in the verses, tap, clap or stomp with Beet and Cherry.

CHORUS 1

Sweet Beets, we've got some!

If you **want some** Sweet Beets, we've got 'em.

If you want Sweet Beets, we've got some,

If you **want some** Sweet Beets, we've got 'em.

VERSE 1

REPEAT   REPEAT

BEET   BEET   CHERRY BEET   CHERRY CHERRY CHERRY   BEET

REPEAT   REPEAT

CHERRY   BEET   CHERRY   BEET   CHERRY CHERRY CHERRY   BEET

CHORUS 2

Sweet Beets, we've got some!
If you **want some** Sweet Beets, we've got 'em.
If you want Sweet Beets, we've got some,
If you **want some** Sweet Beets, we've got 'em.

VERSE 2

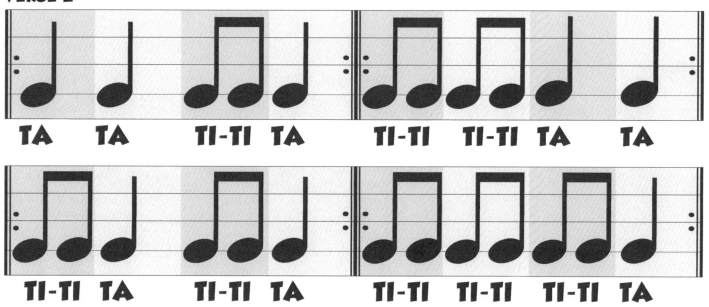

TA   TA   TI-TI TA   TI-TI   TI-TI   TA   TA

TI-TI TA   TI-TI TA   TI-TI   TI-TI   TI-TI TA

CHORUS 3

Sweet Beets, we've got some!
If you **want some** Sweet Beets, we've got 'em.
If you want Sweet Beets, we've got some,
If you **want some** Sweet Beets, we've got 'em.

VERSE 3

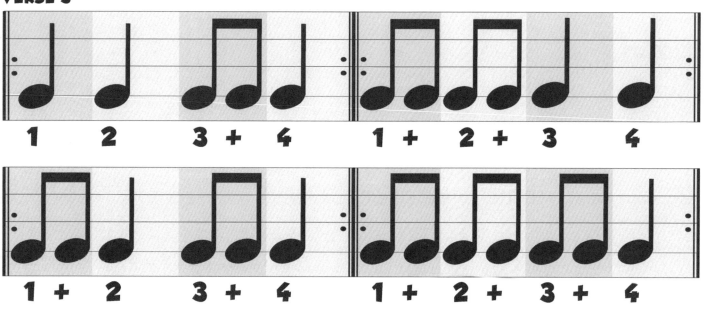

1   2   3 + 4   1 + 2 + 3   4

1 + 2   3 + 4   1 + 2 + 3 + 4

CHORUS 4

Sweet Beets, we've got some!
If you **want some** Sweet Beets, we've got 'em.
If you want Sweet Beets, we've got some,
If you **want some** Sweet Beets, we've got 'em.

VERSE 4

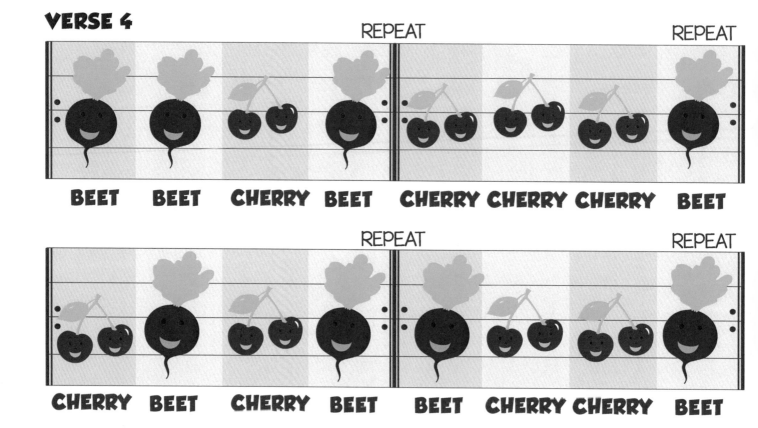

CHORUS 5

Sweet Beets, we've got some!
If you **want some** Sweet Beets, we've got 'em.
If you want Sweet Beets, we've got some,
If you **want some** Sweet Beets, we've got 'em.

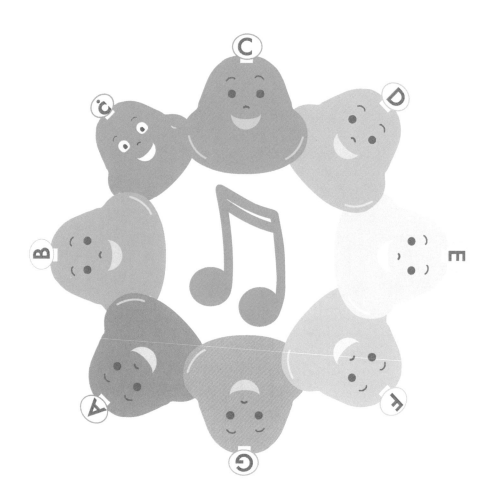

Note Math

In each box, count the number of NOTES. You can look for each individual note head •, or just focus on counting the stems | .

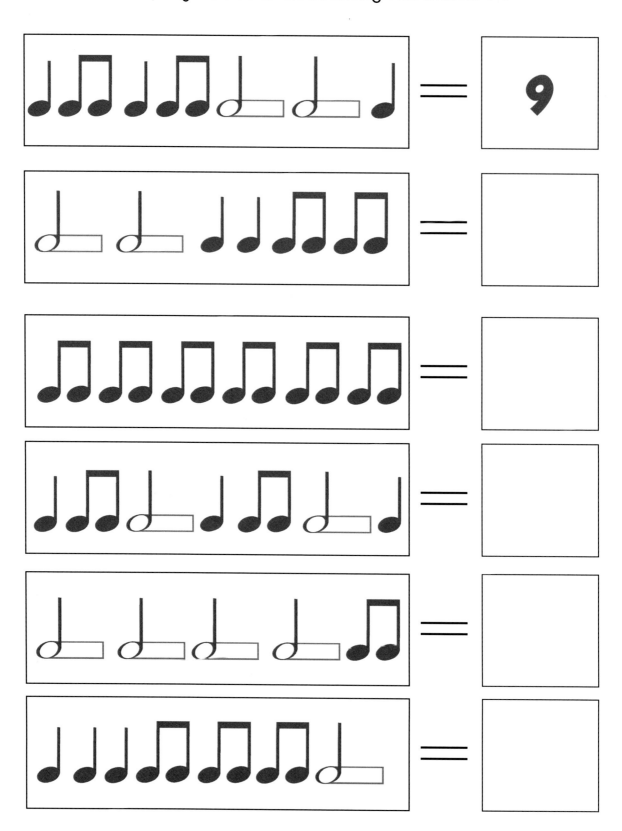

Beat Math

In each row, count the number of BEATS. The Half Note takes up 2 beats. The quarter note takes up 1 beat. It takes 2 Eighth Notes to fill 1 beat.

1 Half Note = 2 beats	1 Quarter Note = 1 beat	2 Eighth Notes = 1 beat

♩ + ♫ = **2**   ♫ + ♫ + ♩ =

♩ + ♩ = _____   ♩ + ♫ + ♫ =

♫ + ♩ = _____   ♫ + ♩ + ♩ =

♫ + ♫ = _____   ♩ + ♩ + ♩ + ♩ + ♩ =

♩ + ♫ + ♩ + ♫ + ♩ =

♫ + ♫ + ♩ + ♩ + ♫ =

Stomp, Clap

Follow along with the patterns below; can you make up your own stomp, clap pattern at the end?

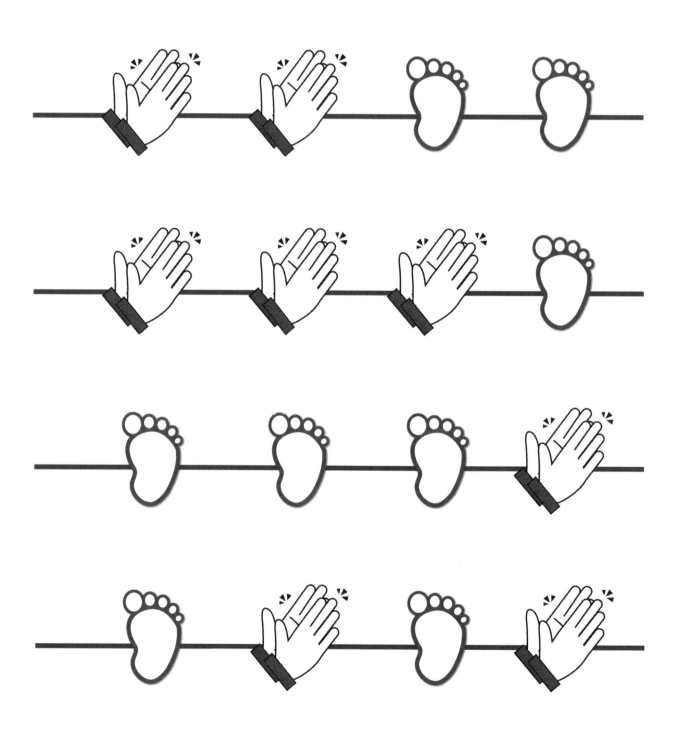

Eighth Notes

You practiced counting quarter notes in section 3.2. Can you count eighth notes at twice the speed?

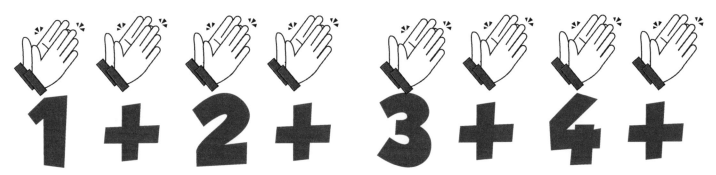

Repeat the top line again! It's a great way to practice keeping a steady beat!

Let's try it again with the Red Bell!

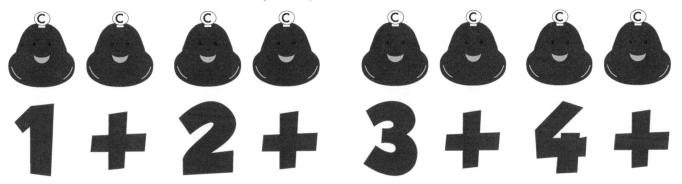

Now let's try it with the **eighth note.**

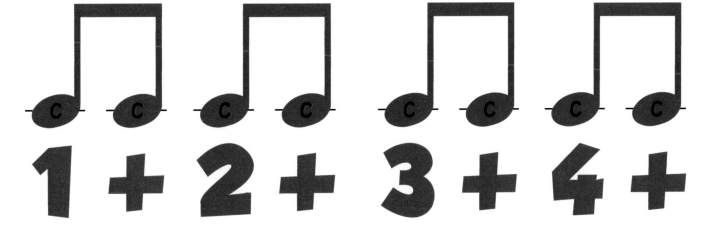

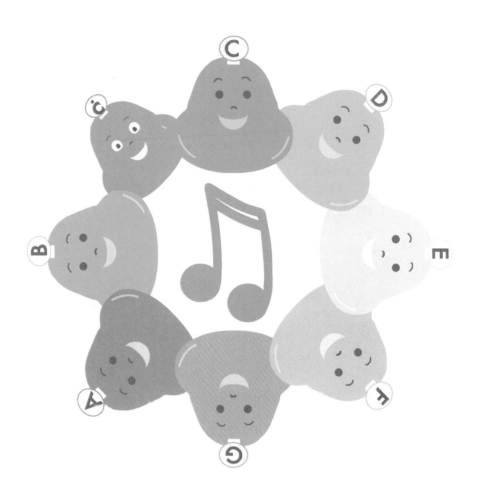

Chapter 3 ✤ Section 4: The Chords on the Bus ♫ Lesson Guide

Objective

By the end of this section, students should be able to play "The Wheels on the Bus" using the I Chord and the V Chord.

Overview

In this section, students use modify chords to play "The Wheels on the Bus".

Essential Question

How can a student play a simplified version of "The Wheels on the Bus" using chords?

Instruction Tips

If students have trouble creating their songs, allow them to work in pairs or work with them to write a new melody.

Materials

- B Bell • C Bell • D Bell
- E Bell • G Bell
- Red Crayon • Teal Crayon • Pink Crayon
- Orange Crayon • Yellow Crayon
- Wheels on the Bus Video Access
- Workbook pages: 46-54

Table of Contents

Complementary Activities

Have your learner share their original songs from the activities in this section.

Section 3.4 Video Annotations

0:35 Pause here and make sure that each learner has their bells set up correctly.

1:08 Pause here and practice the rhythm of the song; make sure students are playing simple, slow chords and not playing to fast.

Wheels on the Bus

Lesson 3.4

☆☆☆☆☆

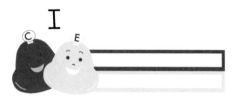 

The wheels on the bus go round and round,

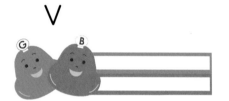 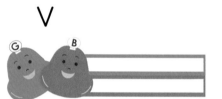

round and round, round and round.

 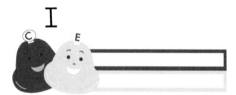

The wheels on the bus go round and round,

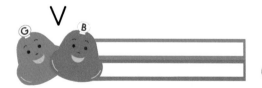 

all through the town.

The mommies on the bus go shh, shh, shh,

shh, shh, shh,   shh, shh, shh.

The mommies on the bus go shh, shh, shh,

all through the town.

The bells on the bus go Do Mi Sol,

Sol Ti Re, Sol Ti Re.

The bells on the bus go Do Mi Sol,

Sol Ti Re through the town.

Ride the Chord Bus

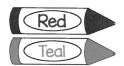

Each bus is carrying one of the chords.
Circle which chord the bus is carrying!
The exact order of the bells does not matter.

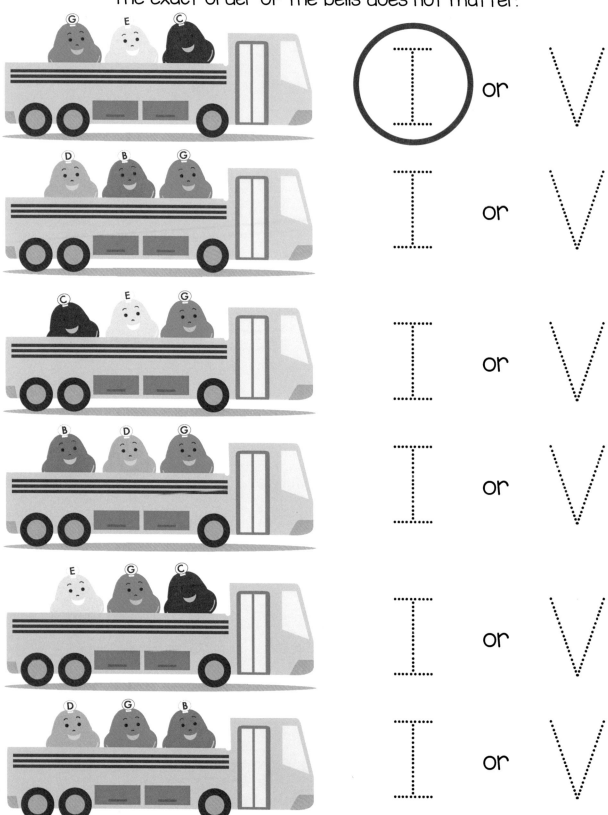

C Chord Song

Cut out the quarter notes on the next page and paste them on top of the gray boxes below to make a quarter note song!

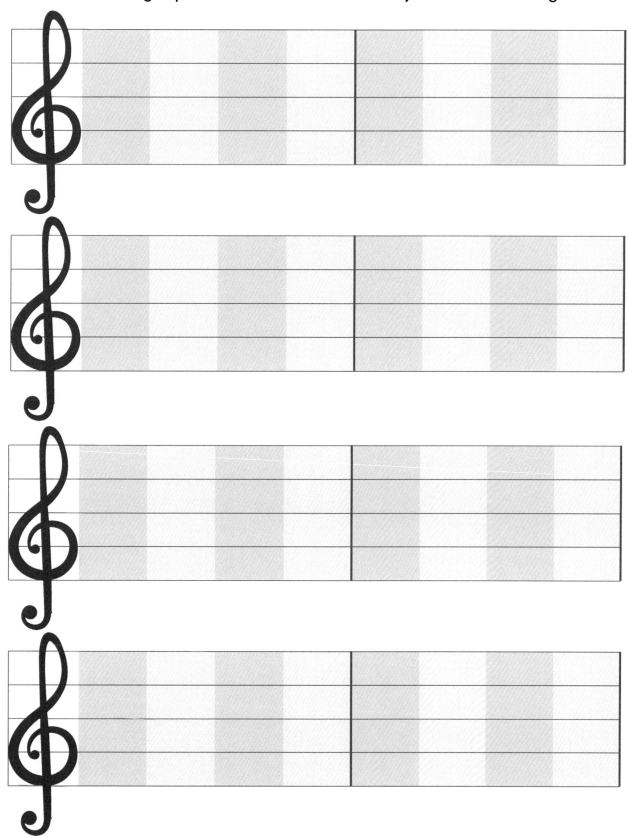

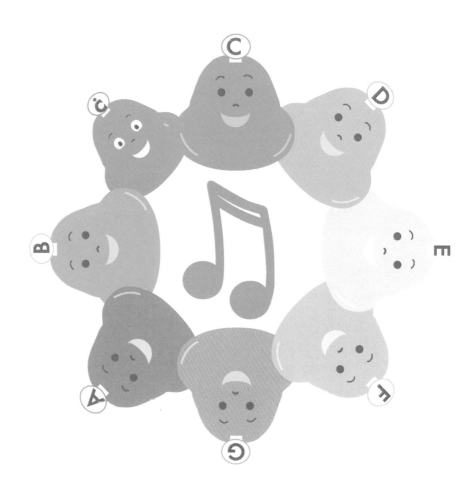

C Chord Song Pieces

Cut out the quarter notes on this page and paste them on top of the gray boxes on the previous page to make a C Chord song!

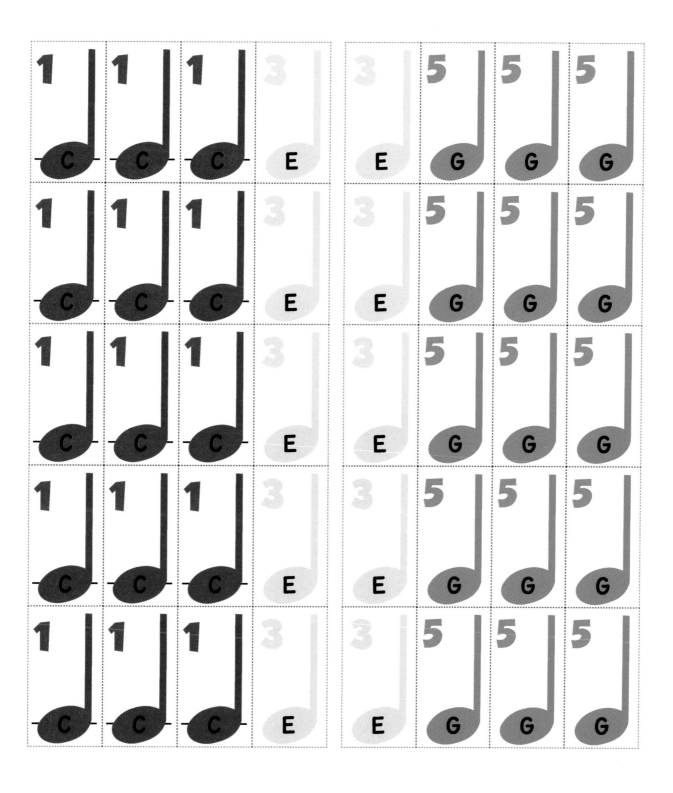

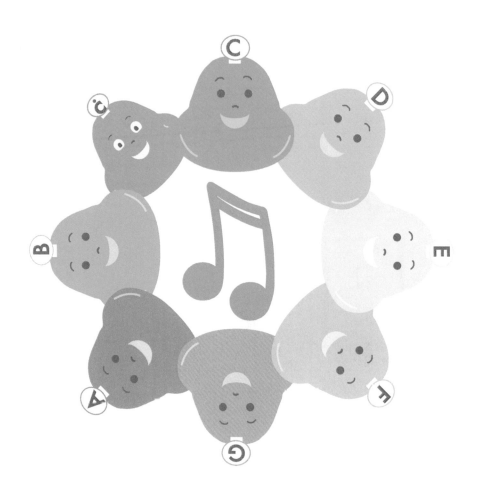

G Major Wheels

Can you count the tires in each pile? Write the number
below each stack, and then grab your bells and play the number song!

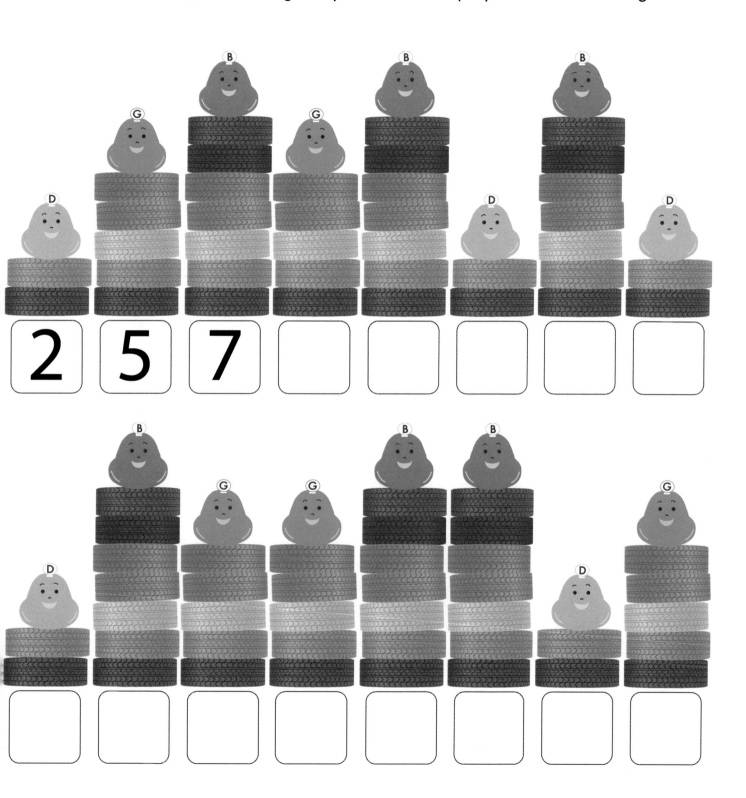

2	5	7					

Compose a 2, 5, 7 Song

Practice writing the numbers 2, 5 and 7!
Only put one number in each box! Then try to play your song with your bells.
Challenge: Write the words to a song underneath the numbers and try to sing
your new song. You can use the different letters of your name instead of words!

| 2 | 5 | 7 | 2 | 7 | | | |

| | | 5 | | | | 2 | |

| 7 | | | | | | | |

| | | | | 2 | | | 5 |

Chapter 3 ❀ Section 5: Chord Watching 2 ❀ Lesson Guide

Objective
By the end of this section, students should be able to distinguish between the C Major Chord and the G Major Chord.

Overview
In this section, students continue to practice with the C and G chords, specifically identification.

Essential Question
How can a student identify the C and G chords?

Instruction Tips
Students may need to watch this video several times before they can differentiate a C chord and a G chord. The more practice they get, the better!

Materials
- B Bell • C Bell • D Bell
- E Bell • G Bell
- Red Crayon • Teal Crayon • Pink Crayon
- Orange Crayon • Yellow Crayon
- C & G Chord Practice Video Access
- Workbook pages: 56-62

Table of Contents

Complementary Activities
Let students take turns playing and guessing the notes and chords. Quizzing another person can reinforce students' memorization of the notes.

Section 3.5 Video Annotations

0:00 Explain to students that they won't be playing the bells with this video; instead, just listening and guessing between the C Chord and the Chord.

1:20 Pause here and let students guess which chord it is.

1:54 Pause here and let students guess which chord it is.

C and G Chord Practice

Lesson 3.5

☆☆☆☆☆

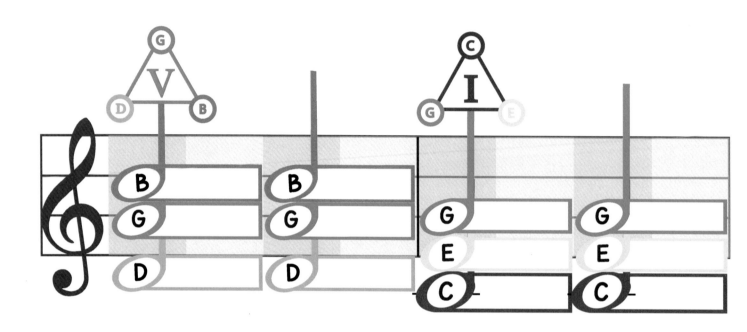

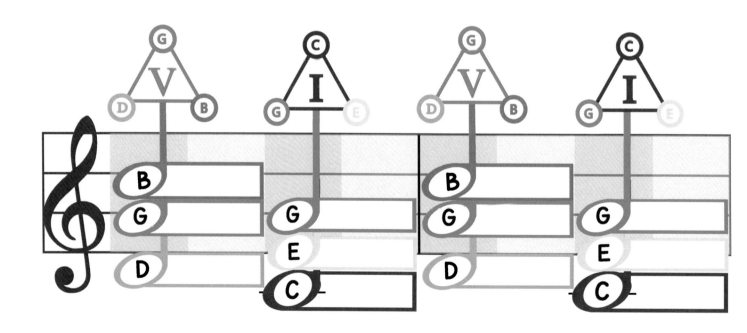

Chord Listening 2

Listening to chords and knowing what chord you are listening to is a big part of building a musical ear!

Cut out the chord cards below and play a listening game.
Player 1 takes the bells and the cards. Player 2 closes their eyes.
Then Player 1 plays EITHER the C Major Chord OR the G Major Card.
Player 2 listens and tries to guess which chord chard they heard.
Record your answers as you play on the next page!

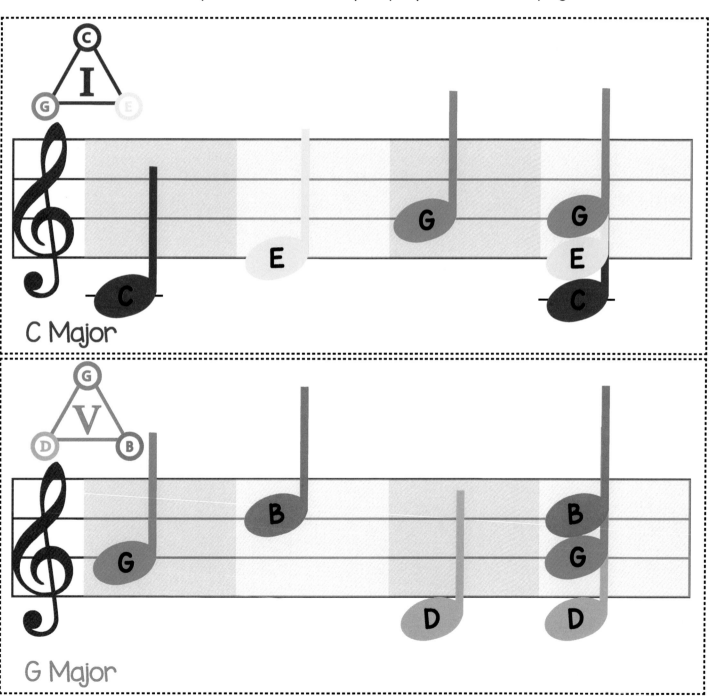

C Major

G Major

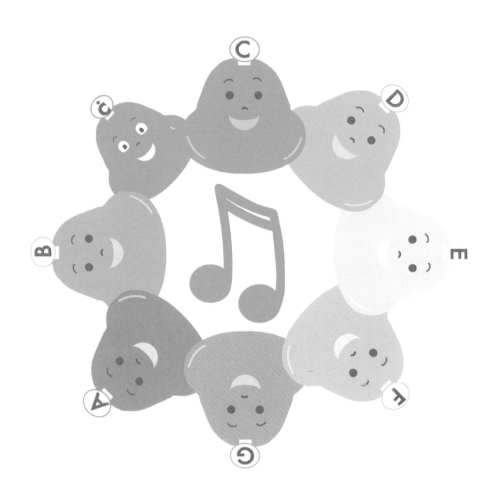

More I & V Listening

Play the Chord Listening 2 Game and use the sheet below to record the chords you think you hear!

1 or   2 or V

3 I or   4 I or V

5 or V   6 I or V

7 I or V   8 I or V

9 I or V   10 I or V

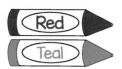

Chord Clouds

Draw a oval around the (G Chords.) Draw a rectangle around the [C Chords.]

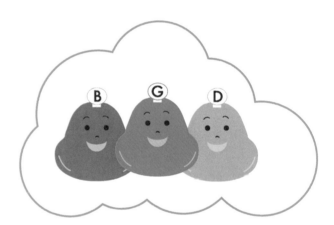

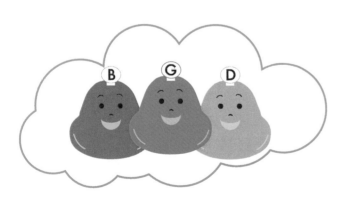

I and V Matching

Draw a line to the bell in each group that matches each corner of the I and V Chords.

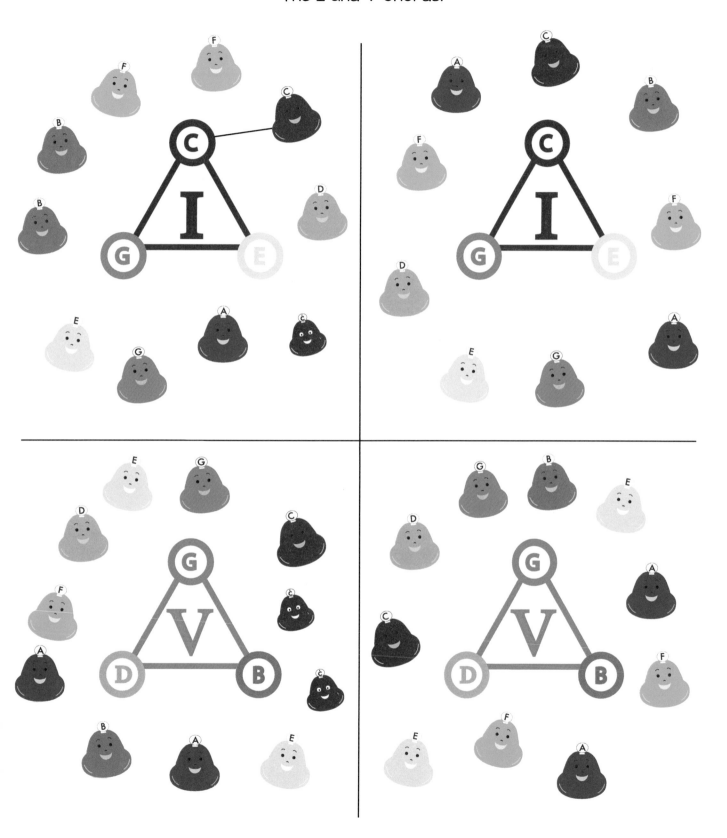

G Chord Boxes

We're looking for some G chords! Can you color the boxes
that contain the notes we need to make a G Chord?
If the box is NOT a G chord, draw an X through it!
Hint: It's okay if the G Chord is not in the same order every time!

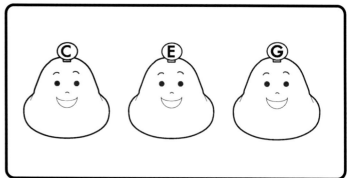

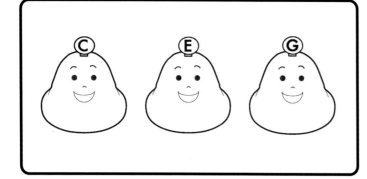
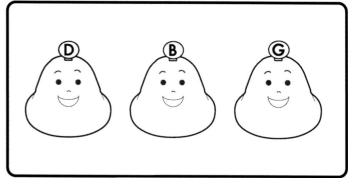

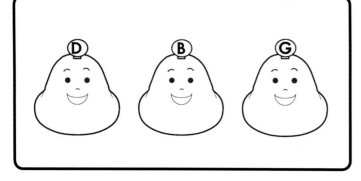
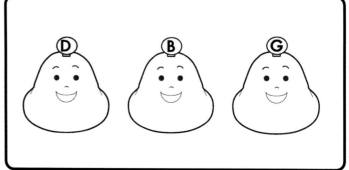

Chapter 3 ♪ Section 6: Bell Balloon Bananza ♪ Lesson Guide

Objective
By the end of this section, students will have had lots of practice identifing C and G by ear.

Overview
In this section, students listen and try to identify the notes C and G without looking.

Essential Question
How can a student differentiate between the notes C and G?

Instruction Tips
There are several activities in this section; you may need to skip some of the activities in order to fit everything into your regularly scheduled music lesson.

Materials
- C Bell • G Bell
- Red Crayon • Teal Crayon
- Bell Balloon Banaza Video Access
- Workbook pages: 64-73
- Scissors
- Tape or Glue
- Popsicle Sticks

Table of Contents

Complementary Activities
Instead of your learner holding up a balloon to indicate their guess, tape the ballons to different corners of the room. Play the bells out of view, and ecourage your learners to run to the correct corner.

Section 3.6 Video Annotations
Find updated annotations in the Prodigies Playground.

Bell Balloon Bananza
Lesson 3.6

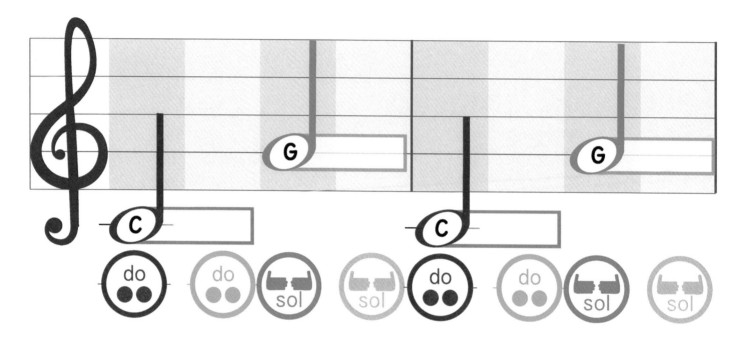

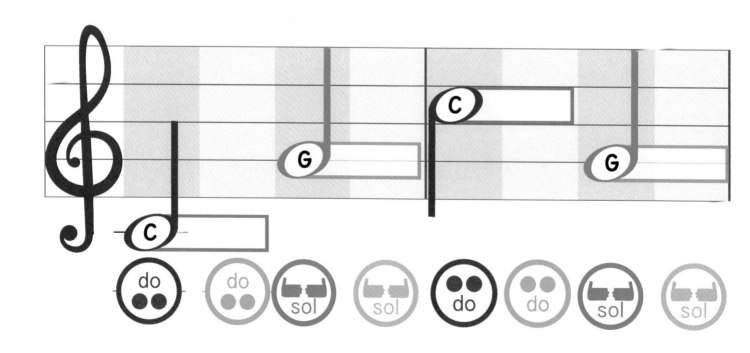

Balloon Puppets

1. Cut out each balloon, and tape or glue it to a popsicle stick.
2. With the bells hidden from the child's view, play one bell at a time and ask the child, "which bell balloon is it?
3. Child identifies the bell verbally OR with the popsicle stick balloons.

If they pick the WRONG note, play them the sound they chose and the correct sound and ask them... "Are these two sounds the same?"

Guide them toward the correct answer and then try again!

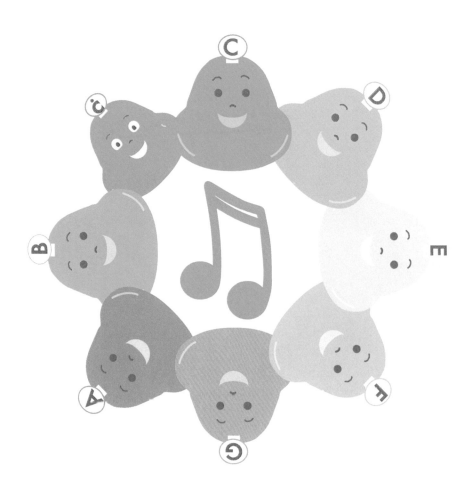

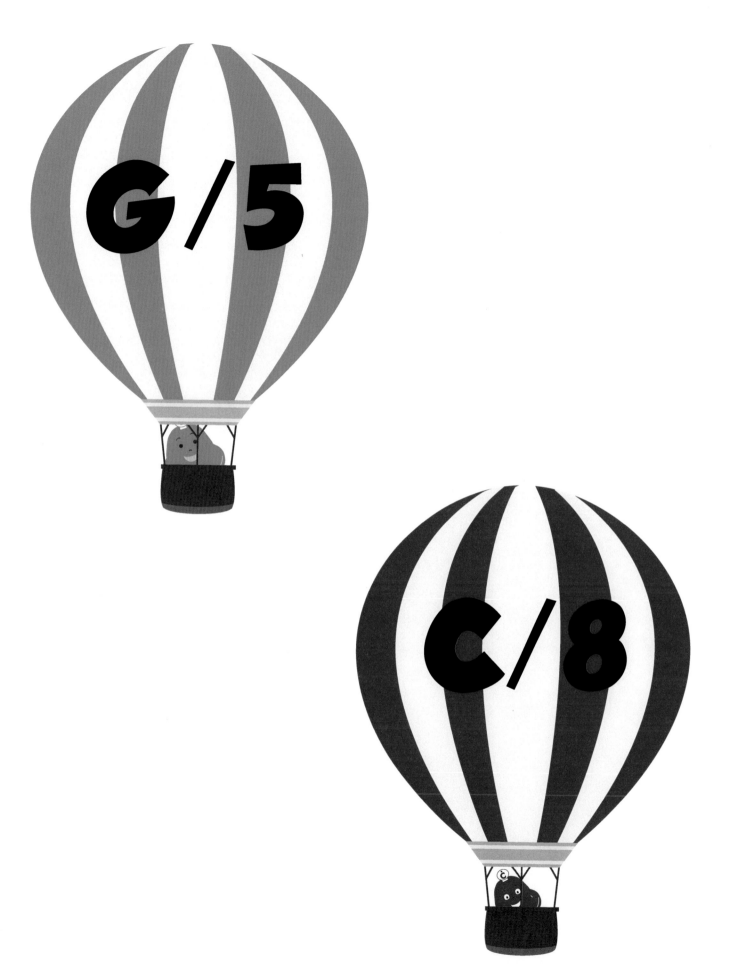

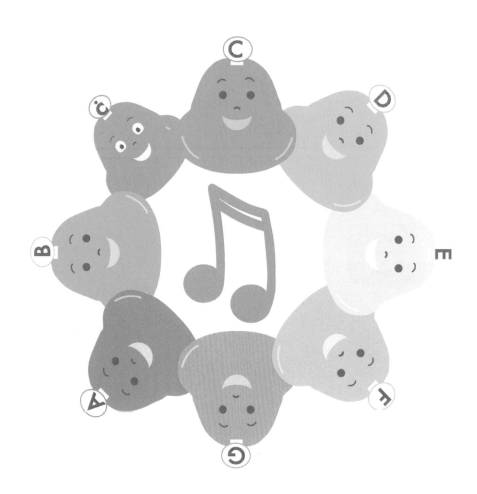

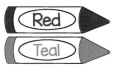

Which Way?

Circle the balloons pointed in the direction written at the top of each box.

← - - - - - - - - - -
Left

- - - - - - - - - →
Right

Hot Air Balloon Maze

Follow the balloons to make it all the way to the end of this maze!

Start here!

You Made it!

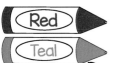

Balloons and Bells

Draw a line between each bell and the balloon with the correct description for that bell.

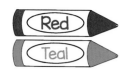

Wrong Way

Circle the bells facing the wrong way in each box.

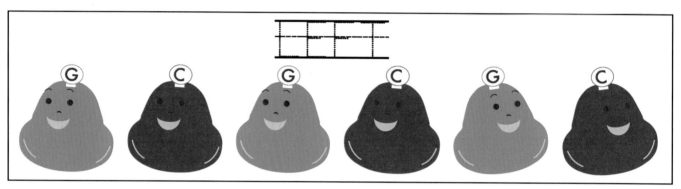

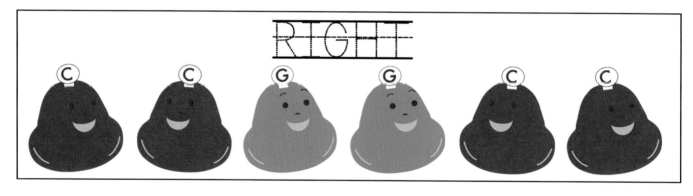

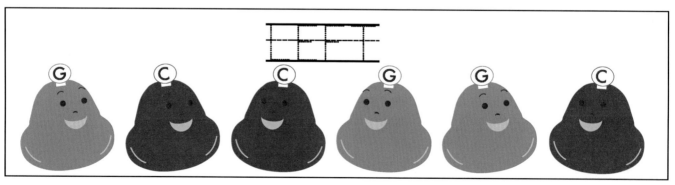

Hidden Bells

Can you find all of the C and G Bells? Write the correct number next to each big bell below!

Chapter 3 ♫ Section L: What Note Is It? ♫ Lesson Guide

Objective

By the end of this section, students should be able to differentiate between B, G and D.

Overview

In this section, students explore the notes B, G and D.

Essential Question

How can a student differentiate between the notes B, G and D?

Instruction Tips

If your students need additional practice, just have them record their answers on a seperate piece of paper, or have them hold up the correct hand-sign to indicate their guess.

Materials

- What Note Is It? Video Access
- Workbook pages: 75

Table of Contents

Complementary Activities

Instead of students guessing along with the video, have them play B, G or D for each other and guess in pairs.

Section 3.L Video Annotations

0:28 Pause and make sure that each student has B, G and D out. Give them time to play each bell and say its note name.

0:45 Pause and let your learner guess the first note name before Rex reveals it!

1:11 Pause and let your learner guess the second note name before Rex reveals it!

1:33 Pause and let your learner guess the third note name before Rex reveals it! Explain to students that this will be the last time you pause before moving on. Be sure that your learner is circling his or her guesses on the What Note Is It workbook page.

What Note Is It?

Draw a circle around the bell you hear in each box!

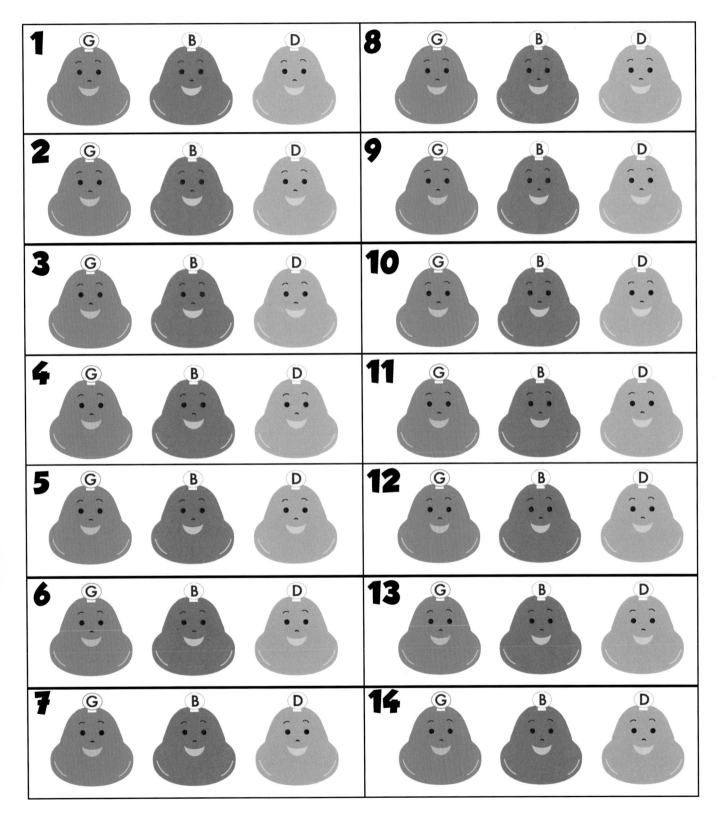

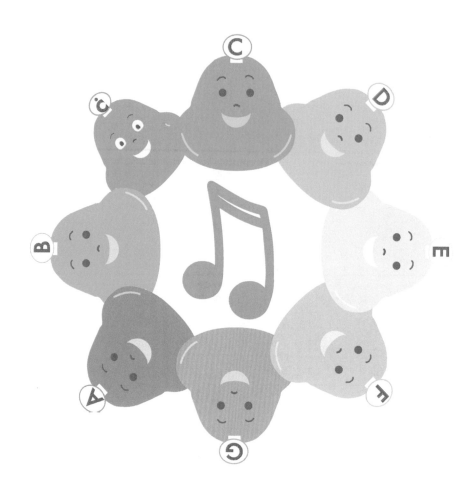

Prodigies Playground
CONGRATULATIONS

You've Completed

Preschool Prodigies

CHAPTER 3

Nice work!

Teacher Signature

Date

52952519R00044

Made in the USA
Columbia, SC
08 March 2019